Hello everyone!

I do hope you'll enjoy my latest *Jacqueline Wilson Annual*. I've tried very hard to fill it full of story treats and creative treasures.

✦ ✦ ✦ ✦ ✩

When I was young, I remember getting *Girl* comic each week and reading it eagerly from cover to cover. So, it was extra-special when I got the *Girl Annual* each year too. It seemed to be jam-packed with all my favourite stories and features, but with all kinds of added surprises.

✦ ✦ ✦ ✦ ✩

Whether you're reading Tracy's birthday story, learning how to sketch my pets, trying out quizzes with your best friends or looking for tips to become the next awesome author, I hope I've squeezed in something for everyone.

✦ ✦ ✦ ✦ ✩

I'll definitely be making some woolly little Circus Ponies. I think they'd look adorable on my Christmas tree!

Love from

Jacqueline Wilson
xxx

THE THREE PAGES I LOVED IN THIS ANNUAL WERE:

Fill in your faves!

1 _____
2 _____
3 _____

A STORY OF DRAMA & DESPAIR!

The Victorians loved tales of desperation and unfortunate events.

Play this game to write your own heart-wrenching story!

Play as many times as you like!

PERSONALITY PICKER

Flip a coin to build a profile for your main character.

HEADS boy	**HEADS** friendly	**HEADS** kind
TAILS girl	**TAILS** lonely	**TAILS** spiteful
HEADS honest	**HEADS** funny	**HEADS** rich
TAILS cunning	**TAILS** sad	**TAILS** poor

HEADS feisty
TAILS meek

HEADS lucky
TAILS unlucky

What will you call your Victorian character?
Why not check out Jacky's historical books for inspiration!

MAGIC NUMBERS

Use your own name to reveal your character's sad circumstance.

1=ABC	**4=JKL**	**7=STU**
2=DEF	**5=MNO**	**8=VWX**
3=GHI	**6=PQR**	**9=YZ**

Use names of friends and family to create different unfortunate events!

○ Add your own numbers of your initials together, for example
HETTY FEATHER (H+F)
IS 3+2 = 5

○ If your number is 10 or more, add the digits together until you get a number between 1 and 9, for example
10: 1+0 = 1

○ Now choose the story that matches your number.

1. Their family has died from influenza
2. Sent to work as a kitchen maid for a cruel master
3. Sells matches on the street for pennies
4. The family loses their wealth and becomes destitute
5. Is robbed in the street
6. Has been abandoned and left to survive alone
7. Is shunned by society because of a disability
8. Has lost their memory after an injury
9. Is forced to perform dangerous tricks for entertainment

BIRTHDAY MATCH

Use the month you were born to choose an interesting feature for your character.

JANUARY - Hair that's long enough to sit on
FEBRUARY - Two different coloured eyes
MARCH - Walks with a limp
APRIL - Never speaks
MAY - Has a spectacular singing voice
JUNE - Has a very noticeable birthmark
JULY - Is blind
AUGUST - Is an amazing actress
SEPTEMBER - Is an excellent thief
OCTOBER - Can't hear
NOVEMBER - Is incredibly beautiful
DECEMBER - Wears a large silver locket

Think carefully about how the circumstance affects your character and work it into your story. For example -

Do they use their acting talents to con people? Perhaps they need the money to buy medicine...

People were very mistrustful of those with disabilities, making it impossible to find work.

Selling hair was a way to make money.

WISHES & DREAMS

What keeps your character going through the toughest of times? Roll a dice to reveal a wish for them —

1. To live with a loving family

2. To become a famous artist

3. To find a cure for a dreadful illness

4. To become rich themselves and care for the less fortunate

5. To live as a writer in a little house by the sea

6. To marry their sweetheart and have their own children

Write down your results to get your story outline!

Turn to page 93 and use the Fortune Finder to reveal a plot for your dramatic tale!

A-Z of JW!

I reveal my A-Z secrets!

A is for Aitken

My surname before I got married. My mum's name was Biddy and my dad was called Harry.

B is for

Bath, the city where I was born. **Battersea Dogs and Cats Home** – I'm an ambassador for this wonderful charity. They do such amazing work for homeless animals.

C is for Cats

My kitty Jacob is so dear to me. I love it when he slinks on to my lap for a little cuddle. Jacob and Jackson my dog both came from Battersea.

D is for Dolls

I've loved dolls since I was a tiny girl and still do. I have a collection of them, old and new. My dolls often appear in my books. Do you recognise this one from *My Sister Jodie*?

E is for Emma

My beautiful daughter. Even though she's grown up now we're the best of friends. We love to visit Paris together.

F is for Friends

I often write about friends in my books. I'm lucky to have lots of lovely friends like Naomi (my publicist), and my best friends, Trish, Chris and Nick.

G is for Greatest

Who else could this be but Tracy Beaker? She's my most famous character and still incredibly popular. Tracy can be quite naughty, but she's also a very brave and brilliant girl.

H is for Hetty

My feisty little foundling has been on so many adventures now. I very much enjoyed writing the Victorian Hetty stories and she's still one of my favourite characters.

I is for Imagination

A good imagination helps me to write. I've always enjoyed entering an imaginary world and was often told off for day dreaming. Once I was even knocked down because I didn't pay proper attention!

J is for Journalist

My first job was working for a teenage magazine. I got the job after sending in a feature I'd written about discos!

K is for Kingston upon Thames

We moved from Bath to Kingston when I was just over a year old and stayed with my Ga and Gongon. I lived there nearly my whole life.

L is for Lola Rose

Jayni has to change her name to hide from danger. To keep her identity a secret, Nick originally didn't draw her picture. But now he's created a cover for the book and you can see exactly what she looks like!

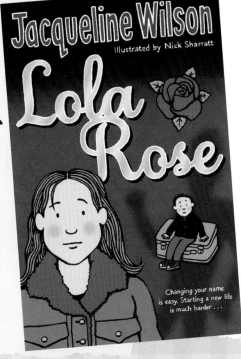

Jacqueline Wilson

Illustrated by Nick Sharratt

Lola Rose

Changing your name is easy. Starting a new life is much harder . . .

M is for Maggots

When I was nine, I wrote my first novel, *The Maggots*. It wasn't very long and it wasn't published. I drew little illustrations for the story and I've kept the tattered notebook safe to this day.

N is for Nick

Nick's illustrations really bring my characters to life. My books wouldn't be the same without them. He's one of my best friends too!

O is for Old-fashioned

I'm not great with gadgets and am very traditional when it comes to writing. I often write things out in long-hand before I start work on the computer.

P is for Presents

I'm very lucky to have received some very special gifts. I've had all sorts of beautiful things made for me by readers, hand-made jewellery, gorgeous shoes and even an *Emerald Star* doll!

Q is for

Queen - my favourite rock band.

The Queen - I've met her a few times.

Queenie - This was published in 2013.

R is for Reading

I'm always reading something. Books, letters, newspapers - you name it, I'm reading it! I have over 40,000 books in my house!

S is for School

I didn't always do well at school — and certainly not at sport or maths! My best subjects were English and Art.

T is for Treasures

I love to wear my bold silver jewellery. I have a big collection now and one of my favourite pieces is this beautiful blue moonstone necklace.

U is for Undies

Tracy Beaker put hers on the top of a tree!

V is for Victorians

I love things from the Victorian era — my old house was Victorian and I have lots of interesting ornaments and knick-knacks from that time. But I'm glad I live in a modern age — I wouldn't want to be a servant like Hetty!

W is for Walking

I go for a long walk every day with my dog, Jackson. We love going to the beach most of all.

X is for X Factor

I enjoy watching reality shows like *The X Factor, Strictly Come Dancing* and *Britain's Got Talent*. It's the perfect way to relax.

Y is for Young

I was only 17 when I moved from the south of England all the way to Scotland for my first job. I stayed in a tiny linen cupboard in a hostel for Young Ladies.

Z is for Zodiac

I used to edit the horoscope column on the magazine I worked for. I eagerly read my lucky stars each week and hoped they would come true. I think they have, don't you?

Lotsa Little

WHICH JW BOOK SHOULD YOU READ?

Follow the arrows to pick a new book!

- Loud OR Quiet?
  - Loud →
- Movies OR Musicals?
  - Movies →
- Computer OR TV?

- Quiet ↓
- Musicals ↓
- Computer
- TV ↓

- Writing →
- Chatting OR Writing?
- Acting OR Singing?

- Real life OR Fantasy?
- Fantasy
- Chatting
- Singing
- Acting

- Real Life ↓

Jacqueline Wilson — QUEENIE

Get the tissues! You love reading sad stories. Is there a happy ending? We can't spoil the surprise!

Jacqueline Wilson — LITTLE DARLINGS

You're hooked on shows like *The X Factor* and finding out the latest star gossip. The story of Destiny and Sunset has lots of celebrity style.

Jacqueline Wilson — EMERALD STAR

There's so much drama and excitement in this Hetty Feather adventure as she sets out to find her father. Drama Queens like you need this book!

FIND A FUN ACTIVITY!

Yo

1 Magazines

What's inside

1 Recipes   **2** Stories

For a birthda

1 Restaurant

The best thing

1 Midnight feasts   **2** Creepy stories

1-4 Brilliant Baking

Get busy making some beautiful cookies or cakes for your friends and family.

9-12 Awesome Artworks

Quizzes!

Fun stuff to brighten up a boring day!

WHAT'S YOUR CREATIVE CAREER?

Answer these questions to find out!

1 Which of these would make you most nervous?

- ☐ Doing a talk for your class
- ☐ Entering an art competition
- ☐ Writing a story for homework

3 You have £10 to spend. What do you buy?

- ☐ Data for your phone
- ☐ Paints and craft stuff
- ☐ A fabulous, sparkly notebook

5 You're most likely to be told off for...

- ☐ Doodling on everything
- ☐ Not paying attention in class
- ☐ Constant chatter

2 You're a brilliant bestie because...

- ☐ You love to make gifts for your friends
- ☐ You keep your pals laughing with jokes
- ☐ You're happy to help out with problems

4 You have an hour to do anything you like. Do you...

- ☐ Design an outfit for yourself?
- ☐ Fill in your diary or scrapbook?
- ☐ Message your BFF?

You chose...

Mostly blue – Writer
You could spend all day making up stories.
Your Task: Start a book club with your BFs to share your favourite tales.

Mostly pink – Artist
You're awesome at art! You love creating pictures.
Your Task: Draw some of your own illustrations for your favourite book.

Mostly purple – Book Agent
You love to meet people and chat. You'd be great at persuading people to publish stories and books.
Your Task: Do a project on your favourite author for a school talk.

(ci)rcle where you fit (i)n the line then add (u)p your numbers to reveal all...

(ar)e...

2	3
Books	Stationery

(...) notebooks?

3
Drawings

(th)at go to a...

2	3
Cinema	Craft party

(...at) sleepovers is

3
Making invites

5-8 Super Story Writing
There's always a new idea buzzing around your brain so get scribbling — it could be the next best seller!

You love arts and crafts, so make a cool collage, (g)et painting or sketch your favourite JW characters.

The ULTIMATE Jacky Q&A

We asked Jacky all about books, writing and life!

If you could only read one book over and over for the rest of your life, what would it be and why?

I'd choose *Jane Eyre* by Charlotte Brontë. I read the first few chapters, when Jane is a little girl, when I was 10 or 11, and thought they were wonderful. I've read the whole book many times since, and never get tired of it.

What's your favourite midnight snack?

I can't resist Pringles.

Would you rather win *Strictly Come Dancing* or *The Great British Bake Off*?

I like watching *Bake Off* best, but I'm rubbish at baking, so I'd choose *Strictly*. I love dancing — but I'd have to be half my age to take part!

How did you know that Nick was the right illustrator for your books?

I think his artwork is wonderful — and as soon as I met him and saw his colourful clothes, I knew he was the right quirky illustrator for my characters.

Did your writing ever get rejected? How did you cope with it?

I've had several novels rejected in the past. It's horribly disappointing — but you just have to try again.

Do you believe in fate?

I think you can decide on your own fate if you try hard enough. But you need a lot of luck and determination too!

What's the fanciest party you've ever been to?

I don't really go in for fancy parties! Still, my publishers have thrown me special book launch parties over the years in posh hotels like the Ritz and Claridge's — and once in the beautiful Lord Leighton museum in Kensington.

What's the best writing advice you've ever had?

I read a little book called *Teach Yourself to Write* by Kathleen Betterton when I was in my early teens and it was brim-full of good advice. She stressed how important it was to show, not tell. For example, the sentence, "Tracy Beaker was a very naughty girl" is nowhere near as interesting as, "Tracy Beaker called Justine Littlewood a very rude name and then kicked her hard on the shins."

TEACH YOURSELF
TO WRITE
K. BETTERTON

If you could rewrite another classic novel like *What Katy Did* or *Five Children and It* which would it be and why?

Maybe I'll choose another E. Nesbit novel — or perhaps one of Noel Streatfeild's books. They're my favourite children's authors.

Is there a character from a book that you particularly relate to? (Not from your own!)

I think I'm a little like Jane Eyre — I used to be poor and plain, I'm imaginative, and I'm very determined.

What was the moment you realised you'd become famous?

I think it was when I went to a large retail park to do a big signing in a bookshop. I saw this immensely long queue and wondered why so many people were gathered there. I was astonished to find they were queuing up to meet me!

If you could rewrite any of your own books, would you?

I think I'd much sooner tackle a new book rather than rewrite one of the old ones. It would be a lot of hard work without the joy of creating new characters.

Apart from Nick, who's your favourite artist? Why?

My favourite children's illustrator when I was young was Eve Garnett, whose most well-known book is *The Family From One End Street*. I used to try to copy her children and make up my own stories about them.

What's your favourite way to relax?

I read or go for a walk with my dog Jackson, or I watch a favourite film.

Have you ever had any special nicknames?

When I was at school one of the teachers called me Jacky Daydream. He also called me Four Eyes when I started wearing glasses!

You've written books in lots of different eras. Is there another time in history you'd like to write about?

I've written about life in late Victorian England. I'm thinking about tackling the middle part of Victoria's reign, when all sorts of interesting things were happening.

If a genie offered to grant three wishes for you right now, what would you wish for?

I'd wish for good health for me and my loved ones. I'd also wish to be able to carry on writing lots more books, and I'd wish for more bookshops and libraries to be opening up — too many are closing down.

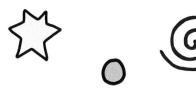

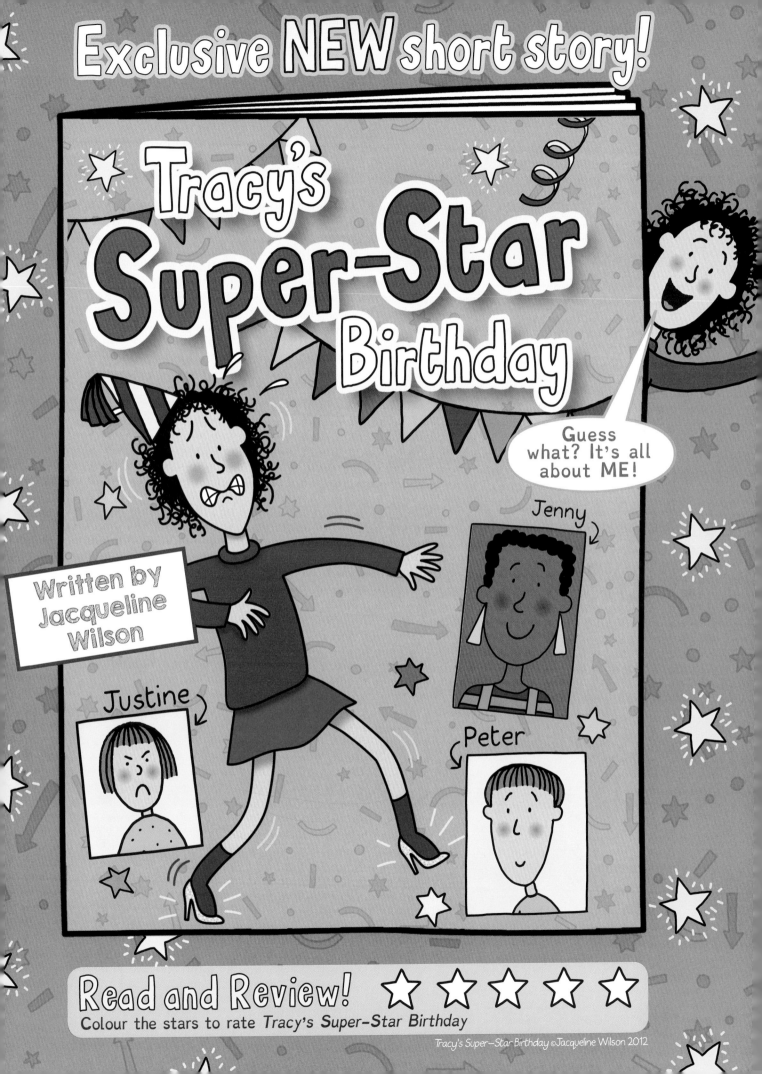

What's the most important day of your life? It's obvious, isn't it? It's your birthday!

My birthday's on 8th May. I bet I had wonderful birthdays when I was little and Mum looked after me. She probably showered me with hundreds of dolls and teddies and cute little bunny outfits — and my own tiny television to fix to the end of my cot, and my own baby laptop with a lovely smiling photo of my mum as a screensaver. But then my mum couldn't look after me any more. I'm sure it wasn't her fault.

Happy Birthday Tracy ~~and Peter~~

★ ☆ ★ ☆ ☆

She just got far too busy and successful being an actress in Hollywood, making film after film. She's still terribly in demand now. But she's going to take a break any time now. She'll drive up to the Dumping Ground in her pink limo and I'll jump in and then we'll be off, Mum and me, and we'll live happily ever after and it'll be just like a movie.

But meanwhile I'm stuck in this rubbish Children's Home and my birthdays have gone rapidly down hill. Especially last year! This weedy little kid Peter had just ended up in the Dumping Ground and you will never ever believe this dire coincidence — his birthday is on 8th May too!
It was as if he'd come along deliberately to spoil my best day of the entire year. He shared all my special birthday treats.

He got jam pancakes for breakfast as well as me. He got cards and presents — and some of his presents were exactly the same as mine. I had this enormous set of very select felt pens all the colours of the rainbow and so did he! He got a special birthday party at the Dumping Ground too. Jenny crayoned a special banner saying *Happy Birthday Tracy and Peter*.
I saw red when I spotted that banner. Still, I had my new set of felt pens. When everyone else was changing out of their school uniform I made a quick alteration. I shortened it a little by crossing out two

superfluous words. The ones at the end. When Jenny saw she was very cross.

'Really Tracy, do you have to be so mean to poor Peter?' she said. 'He'll be so upset when he sees his name crossed off the banner.'

'Call yourself a careworker! You're not meant to say we're mean. You're meant to understand that we're unhappy or angry or insecure!' I snapped. 'And I wasn't being mean anyway. I was simply trying out my new red felt pen to see if it worked properly.'

I nearly ended up being banned from my own birthday party! And guess what — I had to share my birthday cake! Every child in the Dumping Ground gets their very own iced cake on their birthday. You'd have thought the very least they could do was give Peter and me a

cake each. I mean, that's fair, isn't it? But no, we had to share the lousy cake, and that meant we had to blow out the candles together and cut the first slice holding the same knife.

Starz!
Celebs, Celebs, Celebs
Super-Star Birthday Competition

That's when you make your birthday wish. But sharing the cake and the candles and the knife meant I had to share the wish with Peter too. It was only half a wish, so it didn't come true. My mum didn't come to see me. Still, that was last year.

I was determined my next birthday was going to be different. It was going to be the best birthday ever and I wasn't going to let weedy little Peter spoil it. I wasn't sure how I was going to make it happen — until I started browsing through an old *Starz* magazine.

Elaine the Pain, my social worker, lends all her old mags to Jenny. I like to look in them too, just in case I catch a glimpse of my mum. I sometimes cut out pictures of the prettiest ladies, the ones with lots of blonde hair and gorgeous designer clothes and amazing high heels, and stick them on my walls. I tell the other kids they're all photos of my mum. Well, they could be. I was flicking through the pages, looking for blonde look-alikes, when I saw the words **Super-Star Birthday Competition!** My hands started shaking as I read. I couldn't believe it. *Starz* was quite a new celebrity mag.

It started up last May — and to celebrate its first birthday, it was running the most fantastic competition ever. The winner would get a super-star birthday day out as a prize, to share with a special friend. You'd get driven to this ultra-posh hotel in London in a pink limo (just like my mum's!) and then you'd have a fancy lunch with all the magazine people, with an amazing cake specially designed for you by the head chef. A cake all of your own. No sharing!

Then there'd be a special makeover, and a new wardrobe of designer clothes, and they'd do a special photo feature in the magazine. Oh, I badly wanted a makeover! When I was little I used to be cute, with all-over curls, rosy cheeks and a cheeky smile. My mum thought the world of me then. But I seem to have gone off a bit as I've got older. My hair's just this wild frizz no matter how I brush it, and I'm pale and I don't really do smiling much any more.

My mouth seems to want to scowl instead. I really, really, really needed that makeover. Then my mum would feel so proud of me she'd want me with her all the time, no matter how busy she was. I had to win the competition!

You had to write in and say why you wanted a super-star birthday celebration. Well, that was easy enough! I could write pages and pages explaining exactly why. And I'd go on and on about being a poor little looked-after child in the care system, with no decent clothes and hardly any toys, and they'd feel so sorry for me they'd surely let me win! I went rushing off to use the ropy old computer in our living room. Little Wayne was messing around on it, which was seriously bad news. Wayne is one of those kids who always has a runny nose and sticky fingers.

He was actually eating a Krispy Kreme doughnut and jam was leaking out all over the keyboard! 'Yuck! Go and wash, you mucky little boy,' I said, pushing him off the chair. I tried scrubbing at the keyboard with a tissue, to no avail. Wayne started crying because he'd dropped his doughnut when I pushed him. It wasn't really my fault. He shouldn't have been sitting at the computer in the first place.

I nearly burst into tears of frustration too — though of course I never ever cry. I might suffer from a little hay-fever every now and then, but that's not an emotional weakness, it's a medical condition.

'Don't cry, Wayne,' said weedy little Peter, picking up his doughnut and inspecting it. 'It's only a little bit dusty. I'm sure you can still eat the jammy part in the middle. Now stop that silly crying. You're annoying my friend Tracy.' 'I'm not your friend!' I said, glaring at him. As if I'd ever want a little twerp like Peter Ingham as my friend!

He thought he could muscle in and make friends with me just because my true best friend Louise had betrayed me horrendously and gone off with my worst enemy, Justine Littlewood.

'I wish we were friends, Tracy,' said Peter wistfully, looking at me with his big Bambi eyes. I think Peter looks a total weed, and so would anyone with any sense — but he's the sort of big-eyed, blonde, curly haired boy that make old ladies start drooling and calling him a little pet.

He'll get fostered in no time, it's obvious.

'What do you want to write on the computer, Tracy?' he asked.

'It's a secret. Push off!' I said, trying to make the jammy keys work properly. Peter took a couple of steps backwards but still hovered.

I did my best to ignore him and got into the flow of my competition entry. 'Are you writing a story, Tracy?' Peter asked. 'I love your stories.'
'No! Now scram, go on,' I said.

He retreated to the sofa and hunched up in a corner, still watching me intently.
He saw me refer to the magazine article, checking on all the details.
'Are you writing a piece for the magazine all about super-stars?' Peter asked excitedly. 'Oh Tracy, are you writing about your famous mum?'

Justine Littlewood happened to be sauntering down the

Peter

corridor and snorted loudly. 'Tracy Beaker's mum isn't famous, you idiot,' she said. 'Yes, she is! She's a film star and one day soon she's going to come for Tracy and they'll live in Hollywood and make films together,' said Peter.
'You are soooo stupid, Peter. Tracy's been filling you up with a lot of rubbish. Her mum's never ever going to come,' said Justine.

She raised her voice, to make sure I heard. She waited for me to lose it and attack her. But just this once I wasn't going to be goaded.

I needed to concentrate on my competition entry and get it in on time. And then when I won, I'd invite my mum along as my special friend. She loved posh meals and fancy hotels and she'd jump at the chance of designer clothes and a makeover. She wouldn't be able to resist, even if she was right in the middle of making a movie. She'd come running and we'd have the best ever birthday day out. So I carried on tap tap tapping on the jammy computer, telling the magazine just how much it would mean to me to win the competition.

It would be so wonderful to have a really special birthday treat just for me. When you're in a care home you always have to share. Please, please, please let me be the winner! There! I checked the magazine again for the right e-mail address. I was so absorbed I'd forgotten all about Peter. He suddenly bobbed up by my side, peering at the magazine too.

'Oh Tracy, you're going in for a competition!' he said.

'No, I'm not!' I said quickly, trying to snatch the magazine back.

'It's a special birthday competition! Oh wow, you get to ride in a stretch limo and go to a fancy hotel — and you can take a friend!' Peter burbled. 'I'm going to go in for this competition too, and if I win I'll take you, Tracy, and we'll

Justine

have the best birthday ever!'
'I'm going to win, not you!' I said.
'You're not either of you going to win,' said Justine, grabbing the magazine herself. 'You're crazy! This isn't a kids' competition. This is for adults. You'll never win in a million years, Tracy Beaker.'

'Yes I will, just you wait and see!' I said, pressing the little 'send' image. I imagined my competition entry flying through the air and pinging into the magazine editor's computer. I saw her reading it, a big smile spreading across her face. I felt a smile spreading over my face too.

'Look at her! She's on Planet Fairyland!' Justine sneered.

Yes, and it's a wonder I didn't sprout wings and sprinkle fairy dust, because you'll never ever guess what. I did win! I really did, even though it was an adult competition and they had thousands of entries!

'Traceeeeee!' Jenny yelled. 'What's all this about entering a competition? You know perfectly well you should ask my permission first!'
'Jeneeeee!' I yelled back. 'What's all this about reading other people's emails? You know perfectly well you should ask my permission first!'

Jenny would normally tell me off for cheeking her — but she came charging out of her office and gave me a great big hug!

'You've only gone and won!' she said. 'Oh, you're such a crazy kid. Whatever are you going to do next?'

I was so dumb-founded I stood stock still for a moment, speechless. But the Beaker is never at a loss for long.

'I've WON!' I shouted, and I ran up and down the entire Dumping Ground, yelling the good news to everyone. Oh, you should have seen Justine Littlewood's face! It was one of the most glorious moments of my life.

But I was going to have an entire glorious day.

'A ride in a limo, a meal at the hotel, then a makeover,' Jenny read out, bemused.
'Hey, why didn't I go in for this competition myself? It says you can choose a friend to take with you! Who are you going to take, Tracy?'
'Well, I'm not taking you, Jenny, so don't get your hopes up,' I said.

'I think someone will have to come with you from the Home, chickie — but I'm sure you can take a friend too. And I've just had a lovely idea!' said Jenny.

'What?' I saw she was looking in weedy Peter's direction. 'No way!' I said firmly. 'Peter's so not not not my friend. I'm not taking him, not in a million years.'

'Tracy! Keep your voice down! You'll hurt Peter's feelings,' said Jenny. 'Are you sure I can't persuade you? It's Peter's birthday too. It would be lovely to share your super-star day out with him.'

'Tracy Beaker

doesn't do sharing,' I said. 'And I can't take Peter, even if I liked him. I'm taking my best friend ever.'

'Is that me?' said Louise, suddenly all smiles, even though she'd barely spoken to me for weeks.

'No, it is not you!' I said. 'How about taking me, Beaker?' said Justine Littlewood. She really said it!

'You just happen to be my worst enemy, Justine Littlewood. Of course I'm not taking you,' I said. This was getting to be highly enjoyable!

'So who are you taking, Tracy?' asked Jenny. 'She can't take anyone, because she hasn't got anyone who wants to be her friend,' said Justine.

'I have so! I've got heaps of friends,' I said. 'She's got me. I'm her friend,' said Peter, in his little mouse-squeak. 'But it's okay, Tracy, I know you don't want to take me too. You'll want to take your mum, won't you?' Peter Ingham is so irritating! He's too good at guessing.

'Oh Tracy,' said Jenny. 'It's a lovely idea, but I'm not quite sure your mum will be able to make it. She's been out of touch recently.'

'Well, let's get her back in touch. You write to her, Jenny! If you tell her all about the competition, and the makeover and the designer clothes, she'll come, I just know she will,' I said. I wrote to Mum too. I wrote pages and pages and pages.

And then I added a final page with *Please Come* in fancy silver lettering (I borrowed Justine's new pen when they were having a nail-painting session in Louise's room) and then I filled the rest of the space with stars and squiggles and hundreds of kisses.

'That looks simply beautiful, Tracy,' said Peter.

'Why do you have to be such a creep all the time?' I said. 'I don't know. I'm sorry. I didn't mean to creep,' said Peter, and he slunk away. I had a tight feeling in my chest and a squeezy feeling in my stomach then. I often got it when I'd been talking to weedy Peter.

PLEASE COME

I decided the remedy was simple. I'd avoid him at all costs. I also found I had to avoid Justine too, because she discovered her special silver pen was all used up, and she decided for no reason at all that I was the chief suspect. Still, I didn't care about trivial little skirmishes with the stupid kids in the Dumping Ground. I was going to have my super-star birthday outing with my mum. Nothing else mattered.

The magazine got in touch with Jenny to finalise details for the Big Day. I was a little annoyed, as it wasn't Jenny's big day, but she had to give her permission, acting like my parent. 'I've got a parent! My Mum! She'll be coming with me,' I protested.

'Yes, I know that's what you're hoping, Tracy, but we haven't heard from your mum yet. It might not work out quite the way you want. And if she can't make it for any reason, then —

'She'll make it!'

'Tracy, I've tried writing to her and phoning her. Several times.'

'Let me phone her! You're not telling her properly,' I wailed. It's so unfair. She's my mum, yet I'm not allowed to phone her or know her address.
'I've done my best, Tracy,' Jenny said gently.
'Then it's not good enough!' I shouted. 'But she will come, she will, she will, she will!'

I started to get seriously angry and went into one of my royal strops and had to be put in the Quiet Room for a while. I made a lot of noise in the Quiet Room for some considerable time. I didn't cry, I never ever cry, but somehow I ended up with very sore eyes and hiccups. I waited for weedy Peter to come sidling into the room. He usually lends me one of his nan's hankies at such times, and a soothing fruit drop. He didn't come near me this time. Of course I was glad. I mean, who wants that weedy little creep hanging round all the time?

I made a determined effort not to get down-hearted. I'd won the super-star birthday treat and my mum was going to enjoy it with me, I knew it.
I wrote her another letter. And another. And another.
'Are you sure you're sending them to the right address, Jenny?' I said accusingly. Perhaps it was all her fault?

Or perhaps my mum had moved somewhere else entirely? Or

maybe she was ill and couldn't reply? Or maybe she was on location making a movie? She didn't get in touch till the 8th May – my actual birthday. I was up in my room, dealing with a sudden terrible attack of hay-fever, not even feeling like coming downstairs and eating birthday pancakes for breakfast.

'Happy birthday, Tracy!' said Jenny, holding out a parcel. 'I think it's from your mum!' I tore the parcel open. There was a birthday card and a present. I read the message inside the card...

Dear Tracy,
        Have a really great super-star birthday, babe! So sorry can't make it – I'm seeing Uncle Charlie and we're staying at his place.
        Hope you like the present! Party party party!
        Lots of love,
                Mum
                XXX

'She's not coming. She's seeing Uncle Charlie,' I said to Jenny. 'I didn't know you had an Uncle Charlie, Tracy,' said Jenny.

'Neither did I. I can't stick all Mum's uncles,' I said, unwrapping my present. It was a pair of shiny silver shoes with real heels! 'Oh my goodness!' said Jenny. 'Wow! Real grown-up high heels!' I said, trying them on.

They were quite tight. Very very tight, in fact. Perhaps they were a little bit too small. Several sizes, in fact. Mum always forgets I keep growing. But I kept them proudly on my feet.

'Just wait till Justine and Louise see my party shoes with real heels!' I said.
'That's the spirit,' said Jenny. 'So – who are you taking for your super-star birthday outing now?'

'I don't know.' Jenny had that look on her face. 'Definitely not Peter Ingham,' I said firmly.

'You know Peter went in for the competition too?' said Jenny.

'Yes, but he didn't win. I did,' I said, practising walking in my silver shoes. I was a bit wobbly.

'I read Peter's entry. He said he was desperate to win the competition because he knew how much his friend Tracy wanted to have a ride in a stretch limo and a meal in a hotel and a makeover,' said Jenny.

I started to feel wobbly all over. 'I'm not his friend,' I mumbled. 'Anyway, I don't think he likes me any more, not since I called him a creep.'

'Oh Tracy! I think he still likes you very, very much. He's got a birthday card for you. Come downstairs and see it,' said Jenny.

I went downstairs, wincing and teetering in my shoes. Louise and Justine squealed enviously when they saw them. Everyone started singing *Happy Birthday* and Mike started making the pancakes.

I had three cards. One was a big funny one, and all the kids in the Dumping Ground had signed it. There was a red smear of jam beside Wayne's name. There was another card from Mike and Jenny. And a third card, home-made, very long and thin. It was a picture of a long wriggly worm squiggling through lots of blades of grass, but it had Peter's face, with his big eyes and fair curls. It had a speech bubble above its little Peter head.

Happy Birthday, Tracy. I can't help being a creep! Love from Peter.

Peter smiled at me anxiously. He was sitting all hunched up with his head bent. He only had two cards, one from the kids, and one from Mike and Jenny. I had that tight feeling in my chest and a squeezing feeling in my tummy again. So tight and squeezy I could scarcely breathe.

'Just a tick,' I said, hobbling out the kitchen in my high heels.

'Tracy! I'm making you a pancake!' Mike called.

'Yeah, yeah, I'm only going to be a minute,' I said.

I snatched a piece of paper and someone's pen.

I wrote: Happy Birthday little wormy boy. Want to come on my special super-star birthday trip? You'd better say yes! Tracy.

He did say yes. He said yes-yes-yes-yes-yes! The pink stretch limo came and picked us up at 11 o'clock. All the kids crowded out of the Dumping Ground to watch us get in. The chauffeur let everyone pile in together and be driven round the block. But then they all had to get out, and Peter and Jenny and I got in and were driven off in style. It was amazing! The windows were blacked out, but we could still see out, and watch everyone staring at us. We pulled the most terrible faces at everyone! Then the chauffeur played some special music and we sang along. Jenny and the chauffeur sang too!

Then we got to the posh hotel and the magazine people were there to meet us, treating us like royalty. The hotel was soooo shiny and grand that even Jenny came over all shy, but I strutted about in my silver shoes and smiled as if I were a real movie star like my mum. We were led up to our special suite where lunch was served — and you'll never ever guess what! We had our very own butler! He was called Nick and he kept offering us drinks and food, and he called me Miss Tracy! Jenny kept fluttering her eyelashes at him, and whispered that she'd like to take him home with her.

Happy birthday Tracy. I can't help being a creep! Love from Peter.

We sat down at a specially laid table with a snowy white cloth. I kicked off my silver shoes because no-one could see under the table. My toes had such a happy wriggle to be free at last.

I was a bit worried that the food might be very strange and fancy and almost too posh, but it was lovely little bits of chicken and really crispy chips, with our own little bowls of tomato sauce. Then there was a fruit salad with ice cream, and then there was a big pink birthday cake.

'Do you want to blow out the candles and cut the cake with me, seeing as it's your birthday too, Peter?' I said.

'Yes please, Tracy — but you can have my wish,' said Peter. 'My wish has already come true!'

Then we went into the big bedroom for our makeover. The stylist straightened my hair so it wasn't all frizzy and put a little bit of make up on my face, so that my cheeks were pink and my eyes looked sparkly. Then I got to try on all these different incredible outfits. I'd left my silver shoes under the table but it didn't matter. They'd checked my shoe size with Jenny, and had all sorts of different patent pumps and scarlet converse boots and crazy flowery sneakers to go with each outfit.

They took heaps of photos of me to go in the magazine. Some of them were me on my own, but some were with Peter. When the magazine came out there was a caption under the main photo of

Peter and me holding hands and grinning —

Here's our little super-star birthday girl Tracy with her friend Peter on her special day out.

I gave Peter his own copy of the magazine, and I underlined the word friend. I don't know what's the matter with me. I seem to have had a makeover inside as well as out.

I took the remains of my birthday cake back with me and shared it round all the kids in the Dumping Ground. I even gave a slice to Justine Littlewood!!!

Here's our little super-star birthday girl Tracy with her friend Peter on her special day out.

What's Your NEXT READ?

Circle where you fit on the grid below and add up your numbers to find out which JW book you should read next!

Pick a genre...

1	2	3	4	5
Adventure	Fantasy	Drama	Mystery	History

My hobby is...

1	2	3	4	5
Reading	Writing	Sports	Singing	Dancing

On weekends, I enjoy...

1	2	3	4	5
Picnics	Playing at the park	Shopping	YouTube	Sleepovers

Friends describe me as...

1	2	3	4	5
Shy	Dreamy	Daring	Arty	Brave

Pick an item of clothing...

1	2	3	4	5
Baseball cap	Leather jacket	Studded boots	Sparkly high heels	Party dress

5-11 Four Children and It

Lose yourself in a tale of summer picnics and magical wishes coming true! Explore Oxshott woods with Rosalind, Robbie, Smash and Maudie and meet the mysterious Psammead.

12-18 Little Darlings

Imagine if you found out you were related to somebody super-famous! Can two girls who've never met before become best friends and find fame and fortune together?

19-25 Dancing The Charleston

Step back in time to the glitzy, swanky Jazz Age for a daring adventure with Mona. Grab your gladrags and get ready to boogie with *Dancing The Charleston*!

A TOPSY-TURVY DAY IN THE LIFE

What if Nick swapped lives with Jacky?

Wakey-wakey!

Nick usually leaps out of bed as soon as his alarm goes off at 7am, but today he'll curl up and doze for a bit like Jacky would...

Breakfast

Jacky has a cup of Earl Grey tea with a bowl of sliced banana and raspberries and Greek yoghurt on top. How will Nick cope without his usual morning coffee?

Style Switch

Jacky and Nick have very different styles — Jacky prefers black and silver with lots of rings and bangles, but Nick likes to wear colourful shirts and fun patterns!

Work it

Even though Nick likes to come up with lots of ideas in the mornings, he'll have to start writing straight away to fit Jacky's routine! She works on her latest book for a couple of hours, catches up with letters and emails, and even writes articles and plans talks. PHEW, busy!

Break time

This is when Jacky has a cup of coffee and a small snack, or goes out to the village to have coffee with friends. Nick finally gets his fave drink!

Lunch time

Nick will be swapping his usual cheese sandwiches for Jacky's go-to of soup and a slice of bread today. Yum!

Walkies!

In the afternoon, Nick usually does more work. But today he'll get a nice break as Jacky's routine means taking Jackson for a long walk. When she gets home, she curls up with a good book to read for a while.

Evening

In the evenings, Jacky likes to go out to see friends, or go to a pub quiz, to the cinema or even a concert! Very different to Nick's quiet nights in!

Tea time

Nick's favourite food is pasta, so there are no complaints from Nick over Jacky's choice of pasta with lots of vegetables!

Bed time

Time for Nick to herd Jacob and Jackson upstairs, as Jacky usually does each night. Then it's time to get ready for bed... though Jacky often stays up till midnight reading!

THE OCTORAFFE

A day in the life of Jacky wouldn't be complete without writing, so Nick penned this poem...

One end of the octoraffe likes to be wet
And the other end likes to be dry.
One end likes the ocean bed, deep, dark and cold,
And the other, warm sun and blue sky.

One end of the octoraffe likes to be dry
And the other end likes to be wet.
So that is the reason they lead separate lives
And the two ends have never yet met.

WHY NOT?

Have a go at illustrating Nick's poem yourself. Then flip to page 58 to see Jacky's version!

BE AN AWESOME AUTHOR!

A writing tip for every day of the week!

Jacky sits on her chaise longue while writing!

MONDAY

Get Comfortable!
Find somewhere comfortable to write. It could be a desk, in bed, with lots of background noise or in complete silence — whatever works best for you! The more comfortable you are, the more focused you'll be on writing.

TUESDAY

Get Inspired!
You need a topic to write about, so find something that inspires you. It might be something personal, something you've dreamt up or a beautiful picture you've seen. To get started, jot down a few sentences about the story.

Lily Alone was inspired by my walks in Richmond Park!

WEDNESDAY

Plan Your Plot!
Write an outline of your story and who your characters are. This plan will keep you on track if you lose focus!

THURSDAY

Set The Scene!
Now that you've got a story, think about where it's set. It might be a busy, bustling market, an old library or in a boarding school. Write about your story setting here —

....

....

....

32

FRIDAY
Get In Character!

Consider what you like about the books you read — not only is the story important, but the characters are too. Now imagine your character. What are their personality traits? What do they look like? What are their family like? Describe your character in five words:

1. _____
2. _____
3. _____
4. _____
5. _____

Jacky writes before breakfast every day!

SATURDAY
Time Yourself!

Challenge yourself to write for a set period of time — it can be five minutes or an hour, it's up to you! Do this regularly and you'll soon get into a writing habit. Don't be disheartened if you only manage to write a sentence — it will come in time.

SUNDAY
Re-write!

When you've finished your story, it might be jumbled up or contain spelling and grammar mistakes. Re-write your story so that it's neat and makes sense to the reader.

WHAT'S YOUR INSPIRATION?

Pick one choice for each question...

What are you most afraid of?
A) Ghost stories
B) Performing on stage
C) Failing an exam

After reading a book you...
A) Recommend it to a friend
B) Wish you could meet the characters
C) Read it again

What's your favourite hobby?
A) Singing or dancing
B) Reading
C) A sleepover with your BFF

What's your ideal school project?
A) A science experiment
B) A historical topic like the Victorians
C) A talk about your favourite book

Mostly As...
Friends & Family!
You love spending time with other people and you're super-close to your BFF!

Mostly Bs...
Personal Experience!
You're creative and smart — you've got lots of interesting stories!

Mostly Cs...
Books!
You love performing — books, TV and film capture your imagination!

Treasure in the Tower

Party Time!

What has Jodie found in the tower room? Solve all the puzzles to find out!

Melchester College is having a party! Fit everyone correctly into the grid below and a special surprise will appear in the shaded boxes.

Miss French
Undie
Harley
Pearl
Mrs Wilberforce
Jodie
Harriet
Sakura
Clarissa

Put the **2nd letter** of this answer in the **2nd treasure box**.

Pearl

Jodie

Mrs Wilberforce

Harley

Harriet

Sakura

Clarissa

Miss French

Undie

Colour Crazy!

Jodie has dyed her hair a wacky colour — again!

Cross out the letters that appear three times and read the left-over letters to find out what colour she has picked.

KVSWAPRXBX
IPWORBKRAS
XALKEWSBTP

Jodie's hair is _violet_

Put the **6th letter** of this answer in the **1st treasure box.**

Furry Friends

Fill in the missing letter on each line to make two new words. Pearl's favourite animal will appear in the shaded boxes.

THUM **B** OUNCE
DRAM **A** PPLE
BIR **D** RUM
FRO **G** OLF
CHEES **E** MPTY
FEA **R** OBIN

Put the **2nd letter** of this answer in the **5th treasure box.**

Dear Diary...

Pearl has written about a special friend in her diary. Can you work out who it is?

I have so much in common with my new friend! We both love reading and animals — tonight we're sneaking out to watch the badgers! Perhaps this new school won't be so bad after all...

The friend is _Harley_

Put the **2nd letter** of this answer in the **3rd treasure box.**
Put the **3rd letter** of this answer in the **4th treasure box.**

The secret treasure is a...

1	2	3	4	5
T	i	a	r	a

CIRCUS PONY CHARMS

Hetty and Madam Adeline would love one of these cute mascots.

You'll Need

☑ Wool — we used up different coloured left-overs

☑ Googly eyes

☑ Old card from packaging

1 Cut a piece of card that's 22cm long. Wrap wool round 30-40 times to get a thick bundle like this

Choose another colour and tightly tie it in the centre — leave long tails because this will be your horse's bridle.

2 Slip the wool bundle off the card, then lay the bridle wool tails along it like this

3 Fold the bundle in half with the knot at the left end — you should have one tail of bridle wool going down each side.

Cut another piece of bridle wool, wrap it round and round the end to form a nose and tie it in a knot. Leave these ends long too.

Choose another colour and place it under the bundle like this

4 Tie this piece in a bow — now you've made the head! Place the bundle flat with the bow on top like this

Gently bring the two bridle tails together just behind the bow — don't pull too tight. Start to tie knots in the two strings, this will be the mane.

5 When you've knotted to the end of the mane, turn the head back to the side. Now bring the two front bridle tails back to make reins and knot at the back of the head.

Try making ponies from different materials like raffia and embroidery thread.

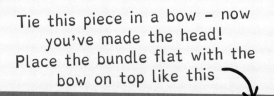

WHY NOT?

Add the googly eyes to finish your pony!

Trim the ends to make a neat edge.

HOW TO PLAY!

On Your Own!

○ Every time you land on a star take a word from the bowl.

○ When you finish write a story about Tracy using every word.

With Others:

○ Cut out the words from the bottom of the page or copy them onto paper.

○ Fold them up and pop into a bowl.

○ Use coins or badges as counters.

○ Roll the dice to move and follow the instructions on each square you land on.

○ Every time you land on a star pick up a word from the bowl.

○ You must make up a sentence using the word before you can move on.

23 ★
24
Miss Brown gives you a gold star! **Jump forward 5 spaces.** **25**
26 ★
27
28 A letter arrives from Mum! Celebrate by moving on 2 spaces.
29 ★
30
31
32
33 Help with the dishes. **Jump forward 5 spaces.**
34 ★
35
36 'Borrow' Adele's make-up and break her eye-pencil. **Fall back 1 space.**
37
38
39
40 ★
41 Elaine-the-Pain finds your Justine Littlewood Revenge Plans. **Move back 3 spaces.**
42
43 ★
44
45 Oversleep for your lunch date with Cam. **Go back 2 spaces.**

FINISH

WHY NOT? Write out more of your own marvellous mammoth words to add to the game!

| Beautifully | Idiotic | Hideous |
| Institutionalised | Enhanced | Stupendous |

You'd love to be a top author like Jacky but writers can hear a lot of 'no's before they get a 'yes'. Have you got what it takes to keep going?

Totally Tracy!

Tracy is disappointed every time her mum fails to visit, but she still believes 100% that Beaker is the Best! You'd never let rejection get in the way of reaching your goals. You're creative and open to new ideas, so there's no problem with taking some criticism to help perfect your amazing writing skills.

YES

You never take 'no' for an answer!

NO

YES

You never accept second best.

Destined To Be A Star!

Destiny didn't stop singing after her disastrous first stage appearance. You can cope too - use rejection as fuel to keep going and show people what you can do. Don't be afraid to big up your best creative skills — being confident in your talent will help make your stories even better.

NO

NO

You wish you were braver.

YES

Brilliant Like Beauty!

Beauty believed she was ugly and dull, but she developed a brilliant biscuit business! Even the most gifted writers have to deal with rejection, so don't let it get you down. Believe in yourself and keep going until you get that one 'yes' - it'll be the only answer that counts!

How to Write A Poem

Anyone can do it!

What is a poem?

A poem is another way to say something or tell a story. You can pick anything you like to write about such as a favourite person or event, time of the year, pet, hobby or thing.

Start by writing some notes on your subject. How will you turn these into a poem? There are lots of different methods, so here are some ideas –

Acrostic Poems

An acrostic poem starts with any name or word and the subject of the poem is based on that word. Writing an acrostic poem is easy and fun, here's how –

Write your starting word so it reads down the page. Now think about what you'd like to say or describe about the word. For example:

Jumping around
And playing in the grass
Cutest little cat
Observing the birds
Basking in the sun

Acrostic poems don't have to rhyme.

A Rhyming Poem

The same lines in each verse should be the rhyming lines. It helps to tap out a rhythm so each verse sounds the same. Look at these examples -

He met a girl with eyes of blue
She was good at cooking too
He knew his love for her was true
A butcher boy called Bertie

To prove to her that he did care
He took her out to see the fair
Some cotton candy they did share
Sapphire and her Bertie

The first three lines rhyme and, although the last lines don't, they end with the same word. You can say the same things with a different rhyming pattern —

Bertie met a fiery girl
With eyes of sparkling blue
And once he'd tried her apple pies
He knew his love was true

He called upon her house one day
They walked out to the fair
He held her hand to show his love
And got treats for them to share

In this one, the second and fourth lines rhyme.

Poems That Don't Rhyme

You can make a poem from something as simple as a collection of random words. Just keep trying the words in a different order until you get something that makes sense. For example -

Hello   Princess   Party
Wander   Have   One   Heaven
Free   Fun   Future   Your
Dream   Visit   Smile
Imagine   Celebrate

Hello Princess
Have fun, party
Imagine your heaven
Wander free
Visit one future dream
Smile, celebrate

What's Your Dream Magazine Job?

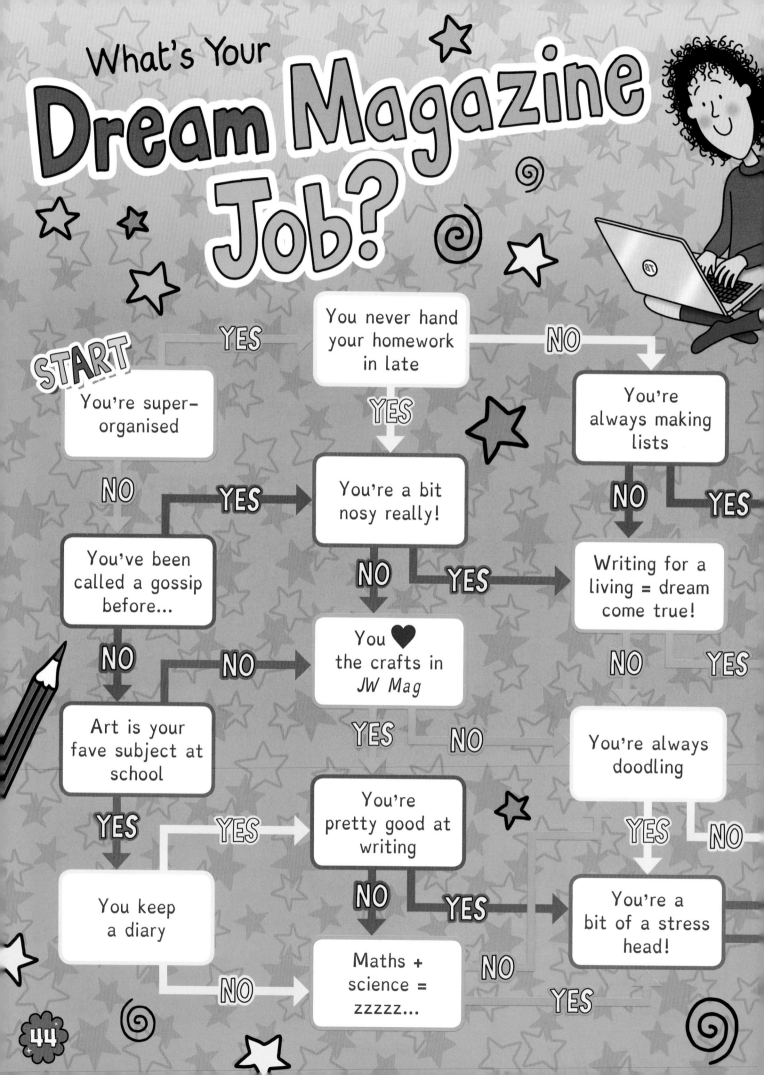

START

You're super-organised

— YES → You never hand your homework in late

NO

You've been called a gossip before...

— YES → You're a bit nosy really!

NO

Art is your fave subject at school

— NO → You ♥ the crafts in *JW Mag*

YES

You keep a diary

— YES → You're pretty good at writing

NO → Maths + science = zzzzz...

You never hand your homework in late — NO → You're always making lists

YES → You're a bit nosy really!

You're always making lists — NO / YES → Writing for a living = dream come true!

You're a bit nosy really! — YES → Writing for a living = dream come true!

Writing for a living = dream come true! — NO / YES → You're always doodling

You're pretty good at writing — YES → You're a bit of a stress head!

You're always doodling — YES → You're a bit of a stress head! — NO

Maths + science = zzzzz... — NO / YES

Starz! Celebs, Celebs, Celebs

Super-Star Birthday Competition

Take our quiz to find out which job is perfect for you!

You'd make a great MAGAZINE EDITOR

You're super-organised and absolutely **LOVE** being in charge, so you'd be great at bossing people around and making sure every page in *JW Mag* was 100% perfect. There would be no dodgy spelling errors getting past you!

YES

NO

You can be a little bossy sometimes!

You'd make a great JOURNALIST!

You love writing and, ahem, being nosy — two things that make an excellent journalist! Well, you might as well get paid for poking your nose into other people's business. Interviewing Jacky would be a dream come true!

You're a bit of a daydreamer

YES

YES

YES

You'd love to interview Jacky!

NO

You'd make a great GRAPHIC DESIGNER!

The graphic designers on a magazine lay out all the text and images and make sure everything looks super-duper pretty — something you would be great at! You're really creative and are always doodling on your jotters!

NO

DONUT FEVER
Do-nutty for these makes & bakes!

DIY Donut Decoration

The perfect prezzy for your BFF!

You'll need:
- ☑ Oven-bake or air-dry clay
- ☑ Paper clip
- ☑ Plastic sprinkles
- ☑ Ribbon

Now hang it on your Christmas tree or pin board. Cute!

1 Roll a walnut-sized ball of donut-coloured clay. Push a pencil or paintbrush through the centre to make the donut hole, then flatten slightly between your hands.

2 Roll another ball of pink clay for the icing. Squash flat and make a hole in the centre, as before.

Mould the edges to make a wavy icing shape and gently press on to the top of your donut.

3 Press the plastic sprinkles into the icing to decorate, then push a paper clip into the clay to create a hanging loop.

Follow the instructions on your clay pack to leave or bake to harden, and tie on some pretty ribbon to finish.

Cactus Donuts

Cutest. Snacks. Ever!

You'll need:
- ☑ Plain donuts
- ☑ Icing sugar
- ☑ Green food colour
- ☑ White squeezy icing tube
- ☑ Flower decorations

Add some flower decorations to some of your cactus donuts to finish. Yum!

4 Use your white squeezy icing to make the cactus patterns — you can copy our ideas from the picture.

1 Mix some icing sugar with water to get a soft, but not too runny, icing paste.

2 Add the food colour a few drops at a time — you can make different shades of green by adding a few drops more.

3 Dip your donuts in the icing to coat the tops, then leave them on a baking tray to let the icing set.

Cactus bakes by Hugh Raine

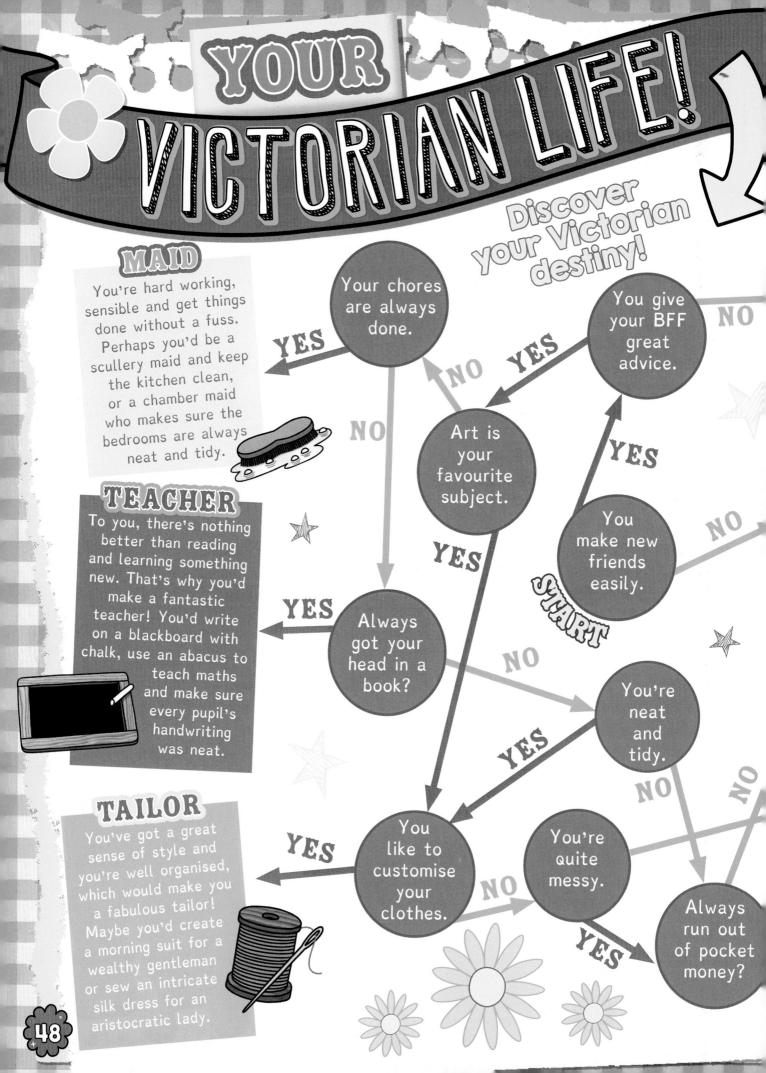

YOUR VICTORIAN LIFE!

Discover your Victorian destiny!

MAID

You're hard working, sensible and get things done without a fuss. Perhaps you'd be a scullery maid and keep the kitchen clean, or a chamber maid who makes sure the bedrooms are always neat and tidy.

TEACHER

To you, there's nothing better than reading and learning something new. That's why you'd make a fantastic teacher! You'd write on a blackboard with chalk, use an abacus to teach maths and make sure every pupil's handwriting was neat.

TAILOR

You've got a great sense of style and you're well organised, which would make you a fabulous tailor! Maybe you'd create a morning suit for a wealthy gentleman or sew an intricate silk dress for an aristocratic lady.

Your chores are always done.

Art is your favourite subject.

You give your BFF great advice.

You make new friends easily.

Always got your head in a book?

You're neat and tidy.

You like to customise your clothes.

You're quite messy.

Always run out of pocket money?

START

YES NO

48

SHOPKEEPER

Your friendly manner and organisational skills would make you a top shopkeeper! Perhaps you'd sell delicious treats in a sweet shop or bakery. Yum! Or how about a toy shop where you could play with puppets and porcelain dolls?

FACTORY WORKER

You're enthusiastic and like spending time with your friends. That would make you an excellent factory worker! You might work in a jute mill weaving fabric or maybe in a printing factory putting together wonderful Victorian books.

VICTORIAN LADY

You'd make the ideal Victorian lady! Imagine being dressed in fine satin and silk and feasting on enormous banquets. You'd also get taken everywhere in a horse and carriage. How sophisticated!

You love shopping.

Confident & outgoing – that's you!

YES

NO

YES

NO

You're super-organised.

YES

NO

NO

You prefer working in a team.

YES

You'd love to be rich & famous.

NO

NO

You like going out for dinner.

YES

YES

YES

NO

ODD JOBS!

Have you heard of these unusual Victorian jobs?

MARSHALL
A horse doctor who fitted horses with new shoes!

WAINWRIGHT
A builder or repairer of wagons.

KNOCKER-UP
Someone who knocked on windows to make sure people weren't late for work.

BLACK BORDERER
Someone who made black-edged stationery for funerals.

49

Wordsearch of Wonders!

Find all of Jacky's favourite things in the wordsearch!

```
O Z F P D J F R V Q Q U R
S B R T W Z Z V B N H I I
J I T R U M E L X A N K I
H O S Z B B V X G G N I Z
T N W Y R A G N I D A E R
P U I D N E U H J P D M K
U L M I H Q H R F W J H C
S A M Z N D N T N C B S W
J A I A W R E D A J G I F
L Q N P E B A L L E T L R
O C G V K W T B B C F G U
O Z L Y R E I F O C O N I
M I H E Z W I V H O P E T
S V R K Q Y U Z N V K Y P
L Q B G C B V A Q Y V S G
```

I. Jacky has thousands of b _ _ _ _ _ . She loves to collect them!

2. Her favourite wild animal is the l _ _ _ _ _ .

3. When she isn't writing, she's r _ _ _ _ _ _ _ .

4. Jacky loves f _ _ _ _ , her favourites are loganberries.

5. S _ _ _ _ _ _ _ _ is her favourite sport.

6. Her favourite colours are black and s _ _ _ _ _ _ .

7. Jacky always buys a new r _ _ _ for her jewellery collection after publishing a book.

8. Growing up, one of her favourite books was about three girls going to stage school. It was called *B _ _ _ _ _ Shoes*.

9. Her favourite character is Hetty F _ _ _ _ _ _ .

10. At school, her favourite subject was E _ _ _ _ _ _ .

Jodie's Fizzy Cola Firecrackers

My super-chocolatey cola cakes have a fizzy surprise!

You'll need:

Cakes:
- 200g plain flour
- 250g caster sugar
- 125g butter or margarine
- ½ tsp bicarbonate of soda
- ¼ tsp salt
- 1 large egg
- 125ml buttermilk
- 2 tbsp cocoa powder
- 1 tsp vanilla essence
- 175ml cola

Frosting:
- 200g icing sugar
- 100g butter or margarine
- 1 tbsp cocoa powder
- 1 tbsp cola

Decorations:
- Popping candy
- Cola bottle sweets
- Sprinkles
- Edible glitter (optional)

What to do:

① Preheat the oven to 180°C and put 12 cake cases in a bun tray.

② Put the flour, sugar, bicarbonate of soda and salt into a large bowl. Stir together and set aside.

③ Beat the egg, buttermilk and vanilla in a separate bowl and set aside.

④ Ask an adult to melt the butter, then add it to the cocoa powder and cola in a pan, heating gently. Mix until smooth then pour into the flour mix.

⑤ Stir well with a wooden spoon, then add the buttermilk mix, beating until it's well blended.

⑥ The cake mix should be quite runny, so use a jug to carefully pour it into your cake cases — don't fill them all the way to the top!

⑦ Bake for 15-18 minutes until springy to touch. Leave to cool.

To decorate:

Beat the icing sugar, butter and cocoa powder together until smooth. Now beat in the cola. Swirl the frosting on to the cooled cakes.

Sprinkle on the popping candy surprise.

Now add all your sprinkles and glitter — use bright colours like fireworks. Pop in a cola bottle sweet to finish off these show-stopping cakes!

WHY NOT?

Make them for a bonfire party?

A-Z of Nick Sharratt

All you need to know!

A ABBA
Nick loves to listen to this group and pop music from the 70s.

B BEXLEYHEATH
Where Nick was born. Now he lives in Brighton.

C CHARLIE AND THE CHOCOLATE FACTORY
This book was one of his childhood favourites.

D DESIGN
He studied graphic design at St Martin's School of Art in London.

E EASTER EGGS
Nick used to design wrappers and packaging for these!

F FRIENDS AND FAMILY
Nick has a younger brother and two younger sisters. His best friend is Jon.

G GOLD BLUE PETER BADGE
He was awarded one of these in 2009.

H HOLIDAYS
You might spot him camping in the Yorkshire Dales!

I ILLUSTRATOR
It's what Nick always wanted to be. He started painting when he was small.

J JACQUELINE WILSON
Nick and Jacky have worked together for over 25 years and are great friends.

K

KEYBOARD
Nick's computer keyboard is covered with grubby pencil marks!

L

LUCKY NUMBER 37

M

MESSY MUDDLE
His art studio is very untidy!

N

NICHOLAS JOSEPH SHARRATT
Nick's full name.

O

ORANGE JUICE
He loves it on his cornflakes!

P

PASTA AND PESTO
Mmmm! It's one of his favourite foods.

Q

QUESTIONS!
Nick is always asked what inspires him and what he'd be if he wasn't an illustrator.

R

READING
He reads Jacky's books a few times before he starts drawing the characters.

S

SLIPPERS
Nick always wears his favourite pair when he's working in his studio.

T

TRACY BEAKER
The JW character he has drawn more times than any other.

U

UNIQUE DRAWING STYLE
Nick's bold, colourful and award-winning artwork stands out on the book shelves.

V

VISION ON
His must-see TV show when he was young.

W

WOODSMOKE
It's his favourite smell!

X

X-FACTOR
Nick's definitely got it!

Y

YELLOW
Nick loves this colour, the brighter and sunnier the better!

Z

ZZZZ...
Illustrating over 200 books is tiring work!

Toast-tillas!

Sweet & spicy treats.

You'll need:
✓ Tortilla wrap
✓ 1 dessertspoon icing sugar
✓ ½ tsp cinnamon
✓ Cookie cutters (optional)

1 Add the cinnamon to the icing sugar and mix together well. Cover a baking tray with baking paper.

2 Use cookie cutters to cut shapes from the tortilla or cut into wedges. Pop on to the tray and toast very lightly under the grill.

3 Turn over the tortilla shapes and dust the sugar mix over the top, then pop back under the grill.

4 Let them brown — the sugar will start to melt and crisp — but take care not to let them burn. It only takes 2–3 minutes.

5 Cool before eating — the sugar will be very hot when they come out.

We're yummy with hot chocolate on a frosty day!

Always ask an adult to help in the kitchen.

Tree Tags

You'll need:
✓ Card from old packaging
✓ Wool scraps
✓ Beads (optional)

Pop-up Cards

You'll need:
✓ Card
✓ Paper scraps
✓ Glue
✓ Pen

3D Trees

You'll need:
✓ Green card or paper
✓ Scissors
✓ Ruler
✓ Pencil

Feels

Make yourself a snack then get crafting for Christmas! Use up your scraps to make cute tree tags, cards and decorations.

1 Cut some triangles from the card. Now copy the picture to wind wool round and round to cover the shape – use any colour you like.

2 Thread a hanging loop through the top and hang on your tree or tie to parcels. You can stick on a little star to finish. So easy!

WHY NOT? Thread on some pretty beads as you go.

1 Cut lots of circles from your paper scraps — why not use up leftover wrapping paper? Cut a selection of different sizes and fold them all in half.

2 Now glue them down on your card in a triangle shape. Start with the smallest circles at the top and only glue down one half of each one.

Add a message and you're done!

Merry Christmas!

1 Fold a piece of card in half and copy the picture to draw on a tree like this. Mark on some straight lines around 1cm apart. Cut along the lines.

2 Open out then, starting at the top, pull one strip forward and push the next one back. Do this all the way down the strips.

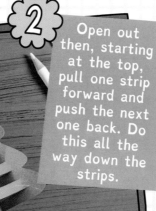

3 WHY NOT? Add some glitter glue or sparkles to your decorations.

57

A TOPSY-TURVY DAY IN THE LIFE

It's Jacky's turn to live a day as Nick Sharratt!

Rise and shine!

Jacky normally snoozes a bit when she first wakes up, but today she'll have to leap out of bed as soon as the alarm clock goes off just like Nick!

Tea vs coffee

Jacky's swapping her bowl of fruit and yoghurt for Nick's breakfast of yoghurt with bran flakes and sultanas along with two slices of marmalade toast. She'll have to wash it down with a mug of coffee like Nick, instead of her usual cup of Earl Grey tea!

Comfy casual

When Nick knows he's spending the day at home, he likes to wear his favourite cardi, cords and comfy slippers. Jacky must feel strange not to be wearing her black and silver clothes!

Inspiration station

Instead of writing, Jacky's going to come up with ideas for illustrations and stories just like Nick does every morning.

Sweet treat

Nick always has an 11 o'clock break to enjoy something sweet. Jacky's in luck — she gets a slice of delicious homemade cake!

Lunch time

Nick likes to have a sandwich, a pasty or a vegan sausage roll for lunch, so Jacky has her pick! Which would you choose?

Artist at work

After lunch, Nick gets on with drawing and colouring up artwork. Jacky has a very special assignment today — illustrate a poem written by Nick!

Jog on

Jacky will have to skip her 4pm snack and go for a jog instead to follow Nick's routine — he goes for a run every other day along the seafront!

Knickerbocker glory

Nick has pasta with a vegetable sauce on the menu for Jacky — it's very similar to Jacky's go-to meal! Except Nick follows it up with a knickerbocker glory made up of anything sweet he can find!

Chill out

After a busy day, Nick likes to relax by watching a couple of episodes of a TV show. Time for Jacky to put her feet up and dig in to a new series.

Sweet dreams

Bed time for Nick is 11pm. Jacky goes to sleep knowing that tomorrow her life will go back to normal and she'll be woken up by Jacob asking for his breakfast.

THE OCTORAFFE

Here's Jacky's illustration for Nick's Octoraffe poem on page 31.

Did you try drawing the Octoraffe? Is your picture like Jacky's?

Ask Nick ANYTHING!

If you could only draw one thing for the rest of your life, what would it be?
Cats. They are a joy to draw.

What is your favourite weird food combination?
Orange juice on my cornflakes.

My weird food combo is:

....

Can you sing? What's your favourite song?
I can't really sing but I know all the words to a song called *The Way We Were* and sometimes get the urge to belt it out on long car journeys.

What advice would you give a young artist starting out?
If you usually draw from imagination, like I did when I was a boy, it's a great idea to try sketching things from real life now and again, to improve your skills.

Sketch something from real life here!

Would you rather go backwards in time or forwards into the future? Why?
I'd like to go back, but only a few decades to the 1960s, because it seemed like such an exciting, optimistic time and I was too young to enjoy it properly!

I want to travel to ....
because ....

Why not use it as a story starter!

What's been your most embarrassing moment as an artist?
There was a spelling mistake on a book cover I'd designed for a famous author. It wasn't actually my fault but it looked like it was, and I was hugely embarrassed. Still am, so I'm not telling you which book it was!

Red Face Ratings

So shameful! ★★★
No way! ★★★★
Major blush! ★★★★★

How embarrassing was Nick's story? Colour the stars!

Red Face Rating – ☆☆☆☆☆

If you could have a superpower, what would it be — and what would you do with it?
I would be able to make time stand still, then I could get all the things done that I need to!

My superpower would be:
....

Who's the coolest famous person you've ever met?
I met the Queen at Buckingham Palace and we were both wearing our gold *Blue Peter* badges. How cool is that?

What's the best advice you've ever received?
'Keep it simple!'

Turn over for more!

Where do you get your inspiration for your own books?
I think about the things that interested and amused me when I was young. I also get ideas from meeting children at book events.

How long does it take to illustrate a full Jacqueline Wilson book?
It depends on the number of illustrations. *We Are The Beaker Girls* took three solid months, but it has hundreds of little pictures.

Which was the hardest JW character to design?
Teenage boys are quite hard to get just right — not too old-looking and not too young. Jordan in the first half of *We Are The Beaker Girls* was a challenge too. If you read the book you'll understand why.

If you could work with any other author, who would it be and why?
It might have been exciting to have illustrated a Roald Dahl story.

What's your dream holiday destination and what would you do there?
Tuscany in Italy. I would soak up the sunshine, stroll around the beautiful towns and cities and feast on fabulous Italian pasta and ice cream.

Jacqueline Wilson
Illustrated by Nick Sharratt
WE ARE THE BEAKER GIRLS

What's your favourite Jacky memory?
We were on holiday and walking through a field of cows, when they started to charge towards us. I ran off like a wuss but brave Jacky calmly stood her ground and shooed them off. I was very impressed!

Is pineapple on a pizza good or bad?
Very bad!

Doodle your fave toppings!

HOW TO DRAW JACKY... AS A CHILD!

It's young Jacky! Sketch her in four easy steps!

1 Draw the oval of Jacky's chin and her ears. Add the curve of her face at one side and the wiggly line of her hair at the other. Sketch in Jacky's neck and the collar of her blouse. Add the curved lines of her arms.

2 Draw in two shoulder straps for Jacky's pinafore. Sketch the front of the pinafore with a slightly wavy hemline. Copy the picture to add Jacky's hair, legs and the outline of her shoes.

3 Now it's time to add Jacky's facial features and short wavy hair. Sketch the cuffs of her blouse and hands. Draw lines for her little white knee socks and the strap detail on her shoes.

4 Add the finishing touches by drawing the checked pattern on Jacky's pinafore and colour her in.

Jacky desperately wanted long hair — try drawing her with a new do!

NICK'S TIP!

Jacky also longed for stylish and sparkly outfits to replace the rather prim clothes bought for her by her mum, Biddy. Design a fabulous party outfit you think Jacky would love.

Don't forget it's the 1950s — find out what fashions were like before starting your creation.

HOW TO DRAW JACKY ...
AS SHE IS NOW!

Sketch the Jacky we know and love! Nick shows you how...

1 Draw a tilted oval for Jacky's cheek and chin then add one ear. Sketch in the zig-zags of her spiky hair. Add Jacky's neck and the curve of her top. Sketch her arms and add a bangle to each cuffline. Draw the rectangle of her body.

2 Give Jacky some more bangles then sketch in her hands. Draw on her glasses. Add her long, slim skirt and the lines of her legs.

3 Sketch Jacky's facial expression then start to add the fine details — a glam necklace, patterns on her skirt and bangles, fabulous high heels and her famous, chunky rings!

4 Now add some colour to your drawing — Jacky loves black, but she also likes navy, silver and beautiful jewel shades like peacock blue and royal purple.

Jacky loves sparkle — use metallic pencils and stick on gems or sequins to embellish your artwork.

NICK'S TIP!

Jacky needs a new outfit for a book launch party. Design something for her to wear here

Remember she'll need shoes and new jewellery too!

How to Draw
JACKY'S PETS!

Nick Sharratt will help you sketch!

JACOB

1. Sketch a curve for Jacob's head and add two pointy ears. Leave a little gap at his chin. Draw a curve for his back and give him one front leg like this.

2. Add a back leg and give Jacob a nose and happy face. Sketch in his other front paw up at his chin, just under his mouth.

3. Sketch a curved tail and give him two little eyes. Add his little tongue licking his paw. Now, sketch in the curve of his tummy.

4. Time for some big whiskers, lines on his paws and ears, and a splash of colour. Jacob has a white patch on his front and on his face, and light grey fur. Don't forget his pink nose and tongue!

Colour in Jacob with lots of tiny pencil strokes to get a fur effect.

JACKSON

1. Start with Jackson's head. He's very furry, so give him zigzag fur on his ear and chin, then add a smiling mouth and a big black nose!

2. Sketch his front and back leg. Copy the picture to draw the curve of Jackson's back — make sure to draw in more furry zigzags! Add a collar, and a ball for him to play with.

3. Finish Jackson's furry body, and give him two more legs and a short, furry tail. Add a little furry line for his other ear, draw circles for eyes and add a disc to his collar.

4. Give him pupils and eyebrows, then finish his collar. Colour him in — he's black all over, with a white tummy, chin and back paws.

NICK'S TIP!

Add some speed lines round Jackson's tail to make it wag!

How to Draw Jess

Draw with me!

Nick Sharratt will help you sketch!

1. Draw an egg shape with two sticky-out ears, then add Jess's neck and body and give her T-shirt a round collar.

2. Add a cloud of hair, then continue the lines of her shoulders into the sleeves of her T-shirt and her arms. Now draw her legs and feet.

3. Sketch glasses from the tops of her ears, then draw her hands. On her T-shirt, draw a large J and add the hems of her sleeves. Now sketch the soles and fasteners of her shoes.

4. Time for details! Add eyes and eyebrows, a big smiling mouth and a nose. Go wild doodling lots of tight curls. Now colour her in!

Can you spot the differences between Jess and Tracy at her age?

70

HOW TO DRAW Mona

Nick shows you how to draw Mona from *Dancing The Charleston!*

1 Sketch an oval for Mona's face, adding a dip on the right side to create the side-on effect. Now, draw her neck, shoulders and the collar line of her dress. Continue the lines of her shoulders into her sleeves, then draw the shape of her arms. Go back and give her two plaits, ending behind her shoulders.

2 Draw two pockets at the ends of her arms, then finish off her right arm. Next, sketch the skirt of her dress, drawing a wavy hemline across. Add her legs, then the outline and straps of her shoes.

3 Complete her left arm, then draw a band across her dress at her hips. Add lines across her legs to give her socks and finish drawing the details of her shoes. Then give her a fringe.

4 Next, give her facial features and finish the details on her collar, sleeves and hemline. Create a flower pattern for the fabric of her dress. Finally, colour her in!

Follow the arrows to reve

Super Sculptor!

You're very intelligent, but you're also patient and kind. You have a keen interest in how things work... and there's no doubt you'd make an amazing sculptor!

Check out Trafalgar Square in London for amazing monuments and sculptures!

Jazzy Jeweller!

You love everything to be bright, bold and beautiful! You're popular and chatty and love everything clothes-related. Why not try being a jewellery designer?

Check out Cartier — the world's most famous jewellers!

SKETCH BOOK

Amazing Illustrator!

You and your besties are an artistic bunch and you like to show them your creations. We think life as an illustrator would suit you best!

Check out how to draw like Nick Sharratt on **page 64**.

74

Art gallery = best day out!

YES

NO

NO

YES

You have a fave artist.

YES

NO

You like reading and drawing equally.

YES

You'd like to travel around the world.

NO

You ❤ customising clothes.

YES

NO

You're always doodling.

YES

NO

NO

YES

You'd be lost without your pens & pencils.

NO

Your projects are neatly typed up.

YES

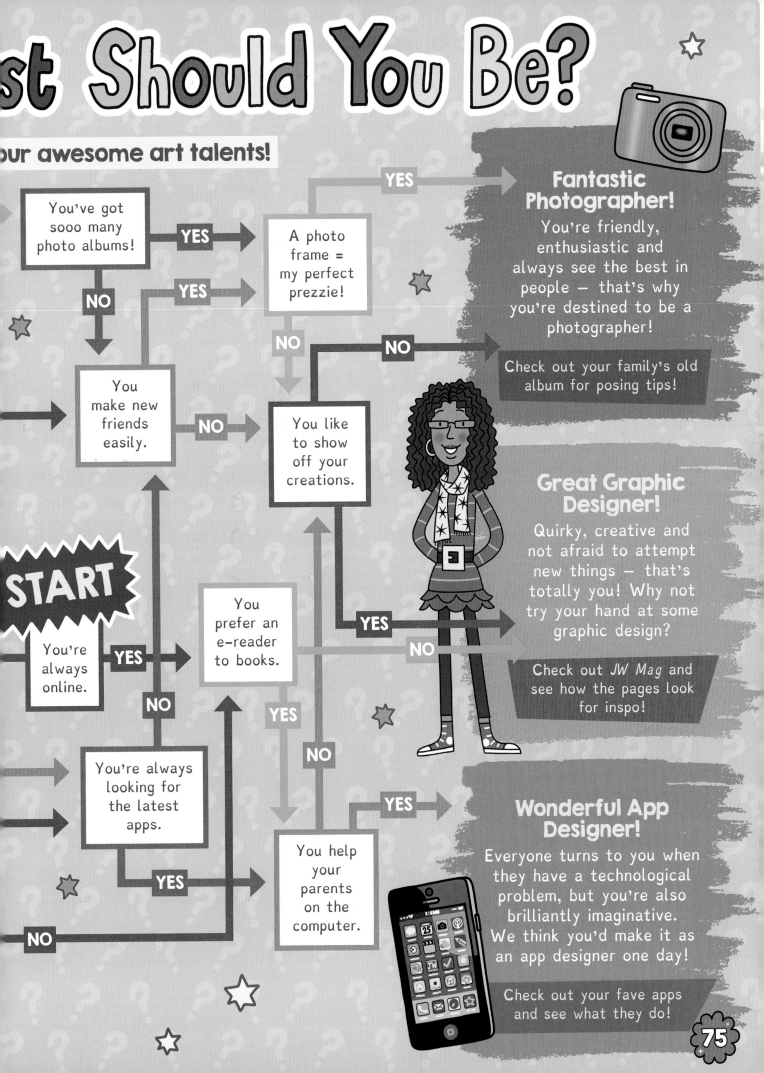

st Should You Be?

our awesome art talents!

START

You've got sooo many photo albums!
YES →
NO ↓

A photo frame = my perfect prezzie!
YES →
YES →
NO ↓

You make new friends easily.
NO →

You like to show off your creations.
YES →
NO →

You prefer an e-reader to books.
YES ↓
NO ↓

You're always online.
YES →
NO ↓

You're always looking for the latest apps.
YES →
NO →

You help your parents on the computer.
YES →
NO ↑

Fantastic Photographer!

You're friendly, enthusiastic and always see the best in people — that's why you're destined to be a photographer!

Check out your family's old album for posing tips!

Great Graphic Designer!

Quirky, creative and not afraid to attempt new things — that's totally you! Why not try your hand at some graphic design?

Check out *JW Mag* and see how the pages look for inspo!

Wonderful App Designer!

Everyone turns to you when they have a technological problem, but you're also brilliantly imaginative. We think you'd make it as an app designer one day!

Check out your fave apps and see what they do!

75

Picnic In The Park

Lily has a special treat packed inside her picnic basket. Solve the puzzles to reveal all...

Kingfisher Mouse Deer Squirrel Rabbit Hedgehog

HIDE AND SEEK

I'm searching the park for Pixie and the twins! Fit these parkland animals into the grid and their hiding place will be revealed.

Rabbit
Squirrel
Kingfisher
Hedgehog
Deer
Mouse

Put the **2nd letter** of this answer in the **2nd picnic treat**. Put the **6th letter** of this answer in the **8th picnic treat**.

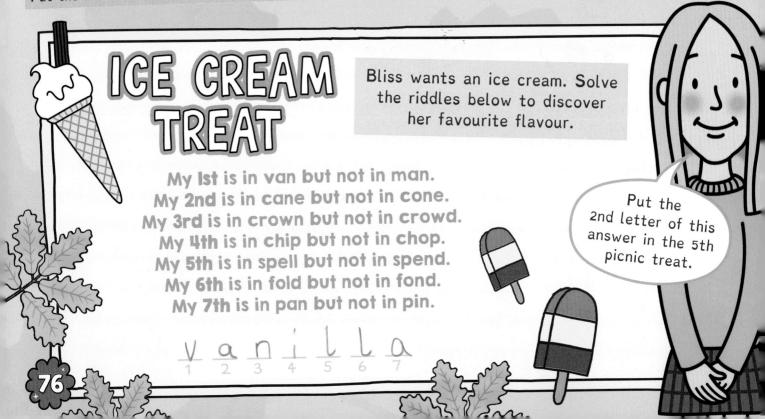

ICE CREAM TREAT

Bliss wants an ice cream. Solve the riddles below to discover her favourite flavour.

My 1st is in van but not in man.
My 2nd is in cane but not in cone.
My 3rd is in crown but not in crowd.
My 4th is in chip but not in chop.
My 5th is in spell but not in spend.
My 6th is in fold but not in fond.
My 7th is in pan but not in pin.

V a n i l l a
1 2 3 4 5 6 7

Put the 2nd letter of this answer in the 5th picnic treat.

SUMMER SPORTS

Uh-oh! Baxter has disturbed a group of people playing in the park

C R I C K E T
1 2 3 4 5 6 7

Cross out the letters that appear three times to find out what game they were playing.

M C A R X
I B M C L
A W K M A
W E B L W
L X T X B

Put the 1st letter of this answer in the 4th picnic treat.
Put the 4th letter of this answer in the 1st picnic treat.
Put the 5th letter of this answer in the 6th picnic treat.

PECKISH POOCH!

Oops! A naughty dog has run off with some of the picnic food! Fill in the missing letter on each line to make two new words. The name of the dog will appear in the shaded boxes.

D R I P A R C E L
F R E E S S A Y
S T U M P R A W N
C L A P I C K L E
T R E E L E P H A N T
B O A R U B B E R

Put the 1st letter of this answer in the 3rd picnic treat. Put the 5th letter of this answer in the 7th picnic treat.

C U P C A K E S
1 2 3 4 5 6 7 8

SUNSHINE

SUMMER SUDOKU

Put the right symbol into each square!

WHAT TO DO:
Each symbol can only appear on one line once, and only once in each mini square, too!

SUITCASE

Unscramble these words to pack the case!

1. EASNGSLSU
2. THA
3. MSANCRUE
4. KIIBNI
5. LWOTE
6. SADALNS
7. SSOTRPAP
8. KBOO
9. ARMEAC
10. TOHSRS

78

FUN TIME!

SCRAMBLE

SCHOOL'S OUT

Test your JW knowledge!

Which family moved to the seaside town of Cooksea?

A. Cookie and her mum
B. Tracy and Jess Beaker C. Tilly and her dad

Who does Tim make friends with at the adventure camp in Cliffhanger?

A. Tiger B. Football
C. Biscuits

In Little Darlings, what is the name of Destiny's sister?

A. Aurora B. Sunset
C. Dawn

Who performed as mermaid Emerald Star at Mr Clarendon's Seaside Curiosities?

A. Rose Rivers B. Clover Moon
C. Hetty Feather

Which character finds a Psammead one summer holiday?

A. Rose Rivers B. Clover Moon
C. Hetty Feather

PASSPORT

FRIGHTFUL FUN!

Perfect puzzles for Autumn!

MONSTER MATCH!

There are **THREE** different version of Eerie Elsa here, but which two are a dead ringer?

A ☐   B ☐   C ☐   D ☐

MIDNIGHT MUDDLE!

Look closely – can you spot the five differences in these two spooky pics that take place during the witching hour? Oooohhh...

CAULDRON CONUNDRUM!

1. A magic drink:
_ _ _ _ _ _

2. Make water hot and bubbly: _ _ _ _

3. Drop in a sticky
_ _ _ _ _ _ 's web

4. Add powdered bat's
_ _ _ _ _
[bats need these to fly]

5. Add a green
_ _ _ _ _ from a dragon

6. Drop in three eyes of
_ _ _ _

7. To mix with a spoon:
_ _ _ _

8. Add a tail from a mouse's big cousin:
_ _ _

9. Pour in a loud
_ _ _ _ _ _ from a banshee

10. Say magical words over the cauldron:
_ _ _ _ _

11. Simmer for 20
_ _ _ _ _ _ _

12. The potion should turn this shade of purple:
_ _ _ _ _ _

13. Drink it from a golden _ _ _ _ _ _

Jacky is concocting a petrifying potion — can you help her find all the ingredients in the square? Unscramble the coloured letters to find out what the potion does!

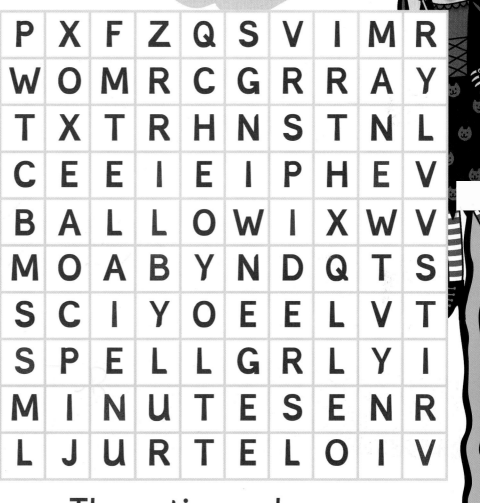

P	X	F	Z	Q	S	V	I	M	R
W	O	M	R	C	G	R	R	A	Y
T	X	T	R	H	N	S	T	N	L
C	E	E	I	E	I	P	H	E	V
B	A	L	L	O	W	I	X	W	V
M	O	A	B	Y	N	D	Q	T	S
S	C	I	Y	O	E	E	L	V	T
S	P	E	L	L	G	R	L	Y	I
M	I	N	U	T	E	S	E	N	R
L	J	U	R	T	E	L	O	I	V

The potion makes you

_ _ _ _ _ _ _ _ _

Cool Quizzes

Chilly Creatures

Can you find these snow-loving animals in the grid?

Huskies   Penguin   Wolf
Moose
Polar Bear   Reindeer
Snow Leopard   Seal
Arctic Fox   Caribou
Narwhal Whale   Puffin

```
E V R V N L Q P V R H D
S L P E A I E T A O U R
O C A E N F E S Q X R A
O C S H G N B F A O K P
M L Z U W D R U B I O O
C B I W A L Q E Z P E E
P N Y L K T A E E Q P L
I W O L F K M H D R T W
L L P O N J J O W S Q O
A R C T I C F O X R H N
U O B I R A C D G K A S
F Z G A R R A M L K A N
```

Snowball Scramble

Which JW characters are hidden in the snowballs?

1.

2.

3.

4.

82

Double Disaster

Whoops! Can you find six differences between these two pictures?

Cool Crossword

How quickly can you solve it?

ACROSS

5. A mug of hot
_ _ _ _ _ _ _ _ _
will warm you up! (9)

7. You wear these on your hands to keep them cosy (6)

8. Whee! You can ride this down a snowy hill (6)

9. A fun winter sport – all you need are shoes with blades (7)

10. These trees are the ones we decorate at Christmas (3)

DOWN

1. In *Starring Tracy Beaker*, Cam and Tracy have egg and _ _ _ _ _ for their Christmas dinner. (5)

2. An icy sculpture made by frozen running water (6)

3. We sing these at Christmas time (6)

4. These animals pull Santa's sleigh (8)

6. This snowy gentleman has a carrot for his nose! (7)

ARE YOU A HOT CROSS HETTY?

Take the tick test to find out!

Your BF turns up to your party an hour late! You...
- ☐ Refuse to let her in. You can't abide lateness! 3 points
- ☐ Grab her in a bear hug and tell her how glad you are to see her. 1 point
- ☐ Welcome her inside, but not before frowning pointedly at your watch. 2 points

Who did you last fall out with?
- ☐ No-one. You can't stand arguments. 1 point
- ☐ Your BF — you bicker a LOT! 3 points
- ☐ Your annoying sibling. 2 points

Dad asks you to help him clean the car. You...
- ☐ Get stuck in — the sooner it's done, the sooner you can start reading JW Mag. 1 point
- ☐ Disappear off upstairs in a boiling rage. It's not your turn! 3 points
- ☐ Mutter 'why me?' under your breath while you scrub the wheels. 2 points

The cat knocks over the clay model you spent hours making, smashing it. You...
- ☐ Shake your fist at the cat and chuck the pieces in the bin. 3 points
- ☐ Fix it with a bit of glue and carefully paint over the cracks. 2 points
- ☐ Start all over again and vow to put it in a safe place this time. 1 point

Pick your ultimate pet hate!
- ☐ L-o-n-g queues! You wait for no-one. 3 points
- ☐ Untidiness. There's just no need for mess. 2 points
- ☐ People with bad manners. It's just plain rude. 1 point

Your pesky brother spills paint all over your fave jumper. You...
- ☐ Wonder what you can wear instead. 1 point
- ☐ Pull a sad face and secretly hope Mum might buy you a replacement! 2 points
- ☐ Clasp the ruined jumper to your chest and wail for hours. 3 points

Now add up your points!

1-6 POINTS
Calm and Collected
Hetty could do with a pinch of your patience! You are level-headed and sensible, no matter what — you're definitely not one to make a fuss!

7-12 POINTS
Quite Cranky!
It can take a lot to get you flustered, but when you do, you can get pretty cross. Remain calm and look at the situation again. You'll soon find a solution.

13-18 POINTS
Temper Tantrum!
Your dramatic and flamboyant personality means you often explode in stressful situations! Try counting to 10 before you react and breathe slowly and deeply.

INSPO BUBBLE BUNTING!

Make your own inspirational garland!

Design your own!

be YOU tiful

BOOKS are MAGIC

GRL PWR

JUST ONE MORE CHAPTER

GIRL GANG

think positive

YAY!

WHAT TO DO:

1. Cut out this page. 2. Cut out the bubble shapes. 3. Thread string through the holes at the top **OR** attach the shapes to a piece of string with little pegs to make bunting.
4. Tie the string at each end and hang it up on your wall.

87

Do or Discuss!

Say bye bye to boredom!

Do It!
Bake something yummy and email a pic to *JW Mag*!

Do It!
Design and colour a TB poster for your bedroom.

Do It!
Write a happy ending for Jess's life story!

Do It!
Start a book you've been meaning to read for ages.

Do It!
Plan your dream party, complete with menus and celeb guests.

Do It!
Make a frame for your favourite photo.

Do It!
Plant some bulbs or seeds.

Do It!
Design a tattoo like Marigold from *The Illustrated Mum.*

Do It!
Help out with a housework chore like dusting.

Do It!
Make a list of all the JW books you still have to read.

Do It!
Give someone a really big hug!

Do It!
Make a card for your BFF.
felt tips

WHAT'S THE PLOT?

How to Play:

- Pick a number between 1 and 4.
- Open and close the square the same number of times.
- Pick a character.
- Open and close again as you spell out their name.
- Pick another character and look under the flap to find your story setting.

Use this to pick a plot for your story of drama and despair from page 3.

DIAMOND

HETTY

1

2

SAPPHIRE

JEM

Your character has invented something with the potential to make a fortune, but other unscrupulous sorts have their greedy eyes on it...

Your character is suffering a terrible time then something happens to change their life completely. Will there be a happy ending – or not?

Your character is offered a way to a better life but it's not by honest means! Do they accept the offer or find another way?

A well-to-do family keeps your character and others in awful slave conditions. How can they escape and get justice for the wrong-doings?

BERTIE

MADAME BERENICE

Will they be able to get it back and will it bring better fortune?

A precious family treasure is stolen from your character. your character is very ill but what happens when they meet someone who promises a cure? Is it real or a con?

Your character befriends an abandoned dog and the two protect each other. But soon it becomes harder and harder and will you ever escape the workhouse?

Your character is sent to the workhouse and bullied by older girls. Can your character stop them to stay together...

4

FREDA

MADAME ADELINE

3

Now you've created a character and picked a story plot so get writing!
Try to work in all your results for tale of drama and despair!

MAKE IT!

1 Cut out the plot picker and turn it over so that the front side faces down.

2 Fold each corner into the centre to make a diamond shape.

3 Flip it over and fold the corners into the middle again.

4 Fold the square in half.

5 Put your thumb and forefingers under each flap and push the four corners together then apart to make the plot picker open and close.